Now y...
violin soloist o... ...g
recorded arrangements

MOVIE
HITS

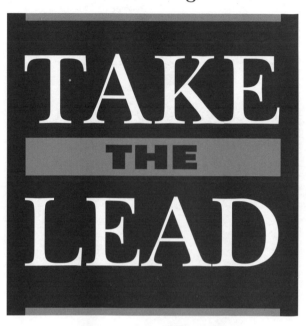

TAKE
THE
LEAD

violin

International
MUSIC
Publications

International Music Publications Limited
Griffin House 161 Hammersmith Road London W6 8BS England

DON'T BE
A MUSIC
COPYCAT!

The copying of © copyright material is a criminal offence and may lead to prosecution.

Series Editor: Sadie Cook

Editorial, production and recording: Artemis Music Limited
Design & Production: Space DPS Limited

Published 1999

International
MUSIC
Publications

International Music Publications Limited
Griffin House 161 Hammersmith Road London W6 8BS England

International Music Publications Limited

England:	Griffin House 161 Hammersmith Road London W6 8BS
Germany:	Marstallstr. 8 D-80539 München
Denmark:	Danmusik Vognmagergade 7 DK1120 Copenhagen K

Italy:	Via Campania 12 20098 San Giuliano Milanese Milano
Spain:	Magallanes 25 28015 Madrid
France:	20 Rue de la Ville-l'Eveque 75008 Paris

WARNER BROS. PUBLICATIONS U.S. INC.

USA:	15800 N.W. 48th Avenue Miami, Florida 33014

Australia:	3 Talavera Road North Ryde New South Wales 2113
Scandinavia:	P.O. Box 533 Vendevagen 85 B S-182 15 Danderyd Sweden

violin

TAKE THE LEAD

In the Book...

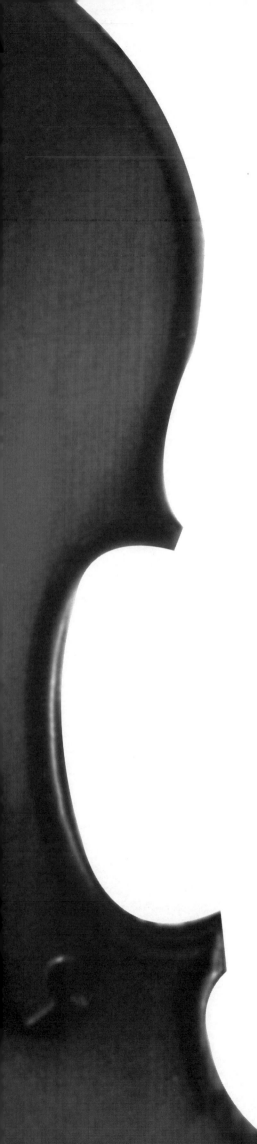

On the CD...

Because You Loved Me

(from *Up Close And Personal*)

Demonstration

Backing

Words and Music by Diane Warren

Rather slow

Blue Monday

(from The Wedding Singer)

Words and Music by
Stephen Morris, Peter Hook,
Bernard Sumner and Gillian Gilbert

Demonstration

Backing

Moderately fast

© 1983 & 1999 Be Music
Warner/Chappell Music Ltd, London W6 8BS

(Everything I Do) I Do It For You

(from *Robin Hood: Prince of Thieves*)

Words and Music by Bryan Adams,
Robert John 'Mutt' Lange and Michael Kamen

I Don't Want To Miss A Thing

(from *Armageddon*)

Demonstration

Backing

Words and Music by Diane Warren

I Will Always Love You

(from *The Bodyguard*)

Words and Music by Dolly Parton

Demonstration

Backing

Star Wars (MainTitle)

Demonstration   Backing

By John Williams

The Wind Beneath My Wings

(from *Beaches*)

Demonstration

Backing

Words and Music by
Larry Henley and Jeff Silbar

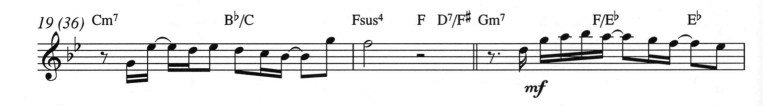

You Can Leave Your Hat On

(from *The Full Monty*)

Demonstration

Backing

Words and Music by Randy Newman

Moderate rock

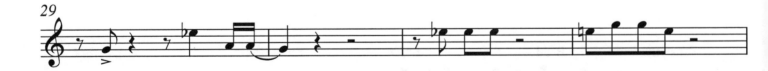

Reproduced and printed by
Halstan & Co. Ltd., Amersham, Bucks., England